KEN'S MERCY FLIGHT TO AUSTRALIA

KEN'S MERCY FLIGHT TO AUSTRALIA

by

BASIL MILLER

ZONDERVAN PUBLISHING HOUSE

GRAND RAPIDS, MICHIGAN

Second Edition, 1945

EIGHT FORTY-SEVEN OTTAWA AVE.
GRAND RAPIDS, MICHIGAN

CONTENTS

CHAPTER 1

THE MERCY FLIGHT

*BY9 calling Island X. Come in, Island X . . . BY9 calling
Island X. Come in, Island X. Give us a bearing.*

The drone of the radioman's voice mingled with the roar
of the Flying Fortress and cut through Ken's mind like a
knife. For thirty minutes the lad listened as Rick, the operator, tried to contact that tiny island, for military reasons
known to the bomber's crew and passengers simply as "X."
It was a dot in the South Pacific, a mere steppingstone for
army planes on their way to Australia.

"If we can't contact them," asked Ken, "what'll we do?"

"We'll set this twenty-five-ton baby down on top of a
wave and in five minutes she'll go to the bottom," said one
of the crewmen. "So, squirt," he continued, calling Ken by
a name which several of the fliers used when speaking to
the young cowboy from Arizona, "if you know how to pray,
you'd better begin pronto."

"What do you suppose I'm doing right now, and have been
ever since we left Washington, D. C.?" asked the lad, who
had been given special permission by the War Department
to make this Australian trip on a B-17 bomber, which was
carrying a precious cargo—far too small to meet the demand
for it—of that miracle drug, penicillin.

Ken looked at the navigator, upon whose reckonings the
bomber depended for directions, then turned toward the
radioman, frantically trying to find a radio station in the
South Seas. A half-hour earlier, at eight o'clock on that
beautiful mid-September morning, the bomber should have
been over the mysterious Island X, on which it was to refuel
for the last lap of a six-hour flight to Australia.

There was no response either from Island X or another station from which cross bearings could be given.

"Pilot to navigator." Ken caught the pilot's words as they came over the plane's intercommunication system, commonly known as the "intercom," and he heard Cory's answer, "Navigator to pilot. Go ahead, Captain."

"Looks like a miss, eh?" said Captain Day, the pilot, whom the crew called Ced. "Dead sure of your reckonings?"

"Absolutely," returned the navigator, "unless something happened to our instruments at Hickam Field."

Then Ken's mind flashed back to their last landing twenty hours earlier at Hickam Field in Honolulu. He recalled nothing unusual about their brief stop during which the plane had been given a routine check by a ground crew.

"The instruments were O. K. to Hickam Field for you hit it on the nose," said the pilot. "Anybody remember anything happening at Honolulu?"

The crewmen, nine in all, spoke one by one into the intercom and none could recall anything unusual.

Ken's mind did a handspring and landed half-awake. He could see the bomber as it was being inspected by the ground crew. Suddenly he remembered a girl who had watched the crew at work. She was small. Her eyes were slanting, but he had thought nothing of this at the time, merely believing that the attractive foreign-looking girl, about five feet, and dressed in ordinary machine-shop girl's clothes, was a member of the ground crew which was giving the plane an inspection.

"Out with it," somebody said, nudging Ken in the ribs with an elbow.

"I was just thinking about the last girl who went into the bomber at Hickam Field. I was half-asleep, but she looked nervous, as if she was afraid someone would stop her. She went inside the bomber and I watched her as she seemed to be inspecting the instrument board, and then she came back here to the navigator's stand."

"Might have been a routine check-up, but I can't see any reason for anybody's being at the navigator's table," said the pilot. "If we believe the worst, then she must have tampered with Cory's instruments, and if she did, there's no telling where we are or where we'll come down."

"Pilot to radio operator . . ."

"Go ahead, pilot."

"Rick, send out an SOS. Say that we have gas for about thirty minutes. Give our approximate location, or where we ought to be. And pound it out to the end."

Ken had been in "tight places" before. But every time he had faced danger, there had been solid earth below him. His eyes glued to the plastic panel through which a wicked-looking machine gun punched its ugly snout, he could see nothing but the blue Pacific, where the winds curled the waves in hill-high heaps. Into his mind crept the assurance of a passage from the Bible. He touched the New Testament which he carried in his shirt pocket.

I will trust, and not be afraid. A verse from the Psalms came to him: *The Lord is on my side; I will not fear: what can man do unto me?*

As Ken's mind raced back to the plane's plight, he heard the pilot say, "Chances are, Rick, she tampered with our sending apparatus, and while we can hear we can't send. We're not only blind without navigating instruments, but dumb as well. O. K., my lads,"—Ken thought he could hear a faint break in the mental tension which ran like a surcharge of electricity throughout the bomber's belly—"better get ready for a rough-and-tumble landing."

"Twenty minutes more to go," said the co-pilot. "Shall we begin to lighten the ship?" He turned to the pilot for the command to cast overboard everything loose.

The pilot, as captain of the plane, gave the order, and the bomb bay doors were slowly opened. Ken watched as through the belly of the ship the crew threw equipment, tools, personal belongings, suitcases, traveling bags.

"Get going, Ken," said the crew engineer, a tall, lanky fellow of twenty-three. "Heave 'er out, the cap commanded."

"Fifteen minutes more," the captain's voice boomed over the intercom.

Major James Kenedy, an army doctor who had played a prominent part in Ken's High Sierra adventure*, stood, holding in his arms a foot-square package. Pilot Day, seeing the package, recognized it as the reason for this special Flying Fortress trip from Washington, D. C., to a United States base hospital, hidden somewhere in Northern Australia.

"Let her go, Doc," said the pilot. "We'll crack up on those waves down there in exactly ten minutes, and every ounce counts. Nothing is more precious than our lives."

Ken's mind leaped the Pacific and hurdled America. He stood once more in a massive White House room. The event was as vivid as when it had occurred, less than thirty-two flying hours before.

Major Jim Kenedy, who had specialized in an army hospital in the use of the new drug penicillin, more effective than anything else on earth in the treatment of certain diseases, had been called into the room. An army attendant had brought the package of penicillin, wrapped carefully in small vials. Because of Ken's part in breaking up the Black Dragon spy ring**, the FBI had prevailed upon the army chief of staff to permit Ken to be a member of the mercy flight which was to carry the drug to Australia, where thousands of boys had been infected by poisoned shells in the South Sea battles.

---

*This story is told in *KEN BAILS OUT*.
**This story is told in *KEN CAPTURES A FOREIGN AGENT*.

"Major Kenedy, I'm entrusting to your care, under the orders of the President, this package of penicillin," Ken could hear the chief of staff say, as he thought about the event. "Upon the safe delivery of this medicine to the base hospital in Australia depend the lives of thousands of our soldiers and sailors. Whatever else you do, *take it through.*

"We're sending you because you know more about the use of the drug than any man alive. You are to deliver the penicillin and then administer it . . ."

Turning to Ken, the general placed his arm around the lad's shoulder and said:

"You are a brave boy and have served your country well in this emergency by breaking up the Black Dragon here in the United States. Although you are too young to be in the armed forces, fighting for the land we all love, I am appointing you as the major's lieutenant. Whatever else may happen, Ken, this penicillin is your special charge."

Ken heard Captain Ced shout, "Five minutes' gas left. Prepare to abandon the plane."

The young cowboy from the Bar-H Ranch in Arizona looked at the altimeter, and saw that it registered 6,500 feet; the plane was more than a mile in the air! He felt the tug of the parachute and the Mae West life belt which he, like all the crewmen, wore, and then his thoughts returned to Washington and he heard the general saying:

"We've given you the finest crew of transport fliers in the world. Captain Cedric Day is our best, and his navigator could chart a course halfway around the world and land on a pin. Remember, upon you and this crew the lives of thousands of our brave lads now depend."

Looking up, Ken saw that Major Kenedy still gripped the package in his arms. Everything was thrown through the bomb bay doors. Ken touched the Testament in his pocket, remembering how precious it had been to him since his mother's death. He remembered a Scripture passage:

The Lord is the strength of my life; of whom shall I be afraid?

Already the crew had taken off their parachutes, for it had been decided that if they had to abandon the plane, or if they should crash, it would be best to make a forced landing, if possible. "This will afford us the use of the life rafts," the captain had told them, "and we will all be together."

Ken knelt on the Fortress floor and began to pray. "Our Heavenly Father, into Thy hands I commend this bomber and these men. Thou knowest how much those boys in Australia need this medicine. They are all shot up with poisoned bullets and infection has set in. They have sent word for this penicillin, which is about all there is in the world. I pray Thee, as the general told us to take the medicine through, whatever else happens, let us get there with it. For Jesus' sake. Amen."

Ken watched as each man threw overboard everything but the clothes which he wore, and then, throwing small mattresses on the floor, the crew braced themselves against the inevitable crash.

"Here, Ken," said the major. "Wrap this around your head."

"Don't forget that when we crash each one is to dive out through whatever opening is nearest—and make it quick," said the co-pilot. "We won't have long to man the rafts. Rickenbacker's Fortress stayed up about six minutes, but most of them go down in two."

Then the crew engineer remembered the few sandwiches and the thermos bottle of coffee which had been left from the night's run, and asked, "Where's the coffee?"

No one recalled having seen it until finally the bombardier admitted that he had thrown it out with the other equipment.

Ken could feel the bomber losing altitude rapidly as his stomach did a quick turnover, and he thought, *Good thing I haven't had breakfast yet* or *it would go overboard.* They had carried with them food for a twenty-hour flight, and had planned to eat breakfast at the refueling Island X.

Ken drew closer to the major, whose arm had gone around the boy's shoulders. He could feel the edge of the package containing the hope of life or death for the suffering soldiers in the hospital, and he breathed a prayer that in the crash the medicine might be saved.

His mind was comforted by the words: *Ask, and it shall be given you . . . Whatsoever we ask, we receive of him, because we keep his commandments, and do those things that are pleasing in his sight.*

Ken felt that, regardless of what might happen, the Lord would enable him to carry the penicillin safely through the crash and on to the hospital where it was so desperately needed.

The long minutes were filled with suspense. The lad could hear the crew praying, some confessing their sins, others begging for mercy. He heard the doctor committing himself into the Lord's hands. "Into Thy hands I commend my spirit," the major was saying, and Ken had a premonition that before the rescue was over there would be many tragedies aboard the four tiny rafts which the bomber carried.

Ken looked up and saw that the pilot and the co-pilot had braced themselves and fastened their safety belts as the giant plane nosed toward the water. Slowly the pilot pulled back on the controls and leveled the plane out as the co-pilot cut the main switch.

"Here she is!" the pilot shouted, and the bomber's tail plunged deep into the crest of a towering wave.

Ken lurched forward and his head struck the back of the pilot's seat. For a moment he thought the world had been blotted out. All went black. The next thing he knew, someone's hands were digging into his clothes and he was being lifted toward an open cockpit. Looking up, he saw the navigator standing over him, with blood streaming down his face from a gash over his eye. Most of the men were already out, but on the floor beside him was Major Kenedy's lifeless form, his face torn and bloody, his skull crushed by the blow.

The lad looked again, and there tightly clutched in his arms was the penicillin package.

Cory was saying, "Come on . . . come on . . . Not a minute to waste. Wanta go down with this thing? We're the last."

Ken heard a voice saying, as if from a great distance, "Whatever happens, you are to take this medicine through to the hospital . . . lives depend upon your being faithful to this trust."

Ken jerked loose from Cory and dived for the package. Then he leaped into the cockpit. Cory had already climbed into the opening. The plane was settling and he could feel the waters as they crept above the bottom of the ship.

Ken saw the crew engineer out on the wings, struggling with a rubber life raft, and beyond him two lifeboats, each containing three men, were bobbing on the waves. Ken knew the smaller of the boats was fastened somewhere inside the bomber, and had not been blown clear by the automatic explosion which forced them out of their places in the bomber's doors. Looking back into the plane, Ken could see only one open door, and he knew his hope of saving the penicillin lay in that lifeboat, which was large enough for only two men.

Handing Cory the package, Ken dived through the open door, into the waters, and fought his way to the other side of the Fortress. As his fingers groped for what he thought was the door on the opposite side, he felt the tangled rope of the rubber boat which was fastened to a broken piece of metal.

He realized that the plane was sinking rapidly. He could

feel the water closing in upon the B-17, and he sensed that he had waited too long.

He was trapped—and the plane was going down.

He had done his best, but it had not been good enough. His lungs burned as he fought to hold his breath in an attempt to shut the water out of them.

Pulling at the tangled rope, he fought for strength to loosen it, but it would not give. *If I go back up,* he thought, *there will be no room for the penicillin.* At that moment he made the greatest decision of his life:

I must give my life for the boys who are dying for their native land.

As he prayed for strength, he felt the rope give way, and the rubber boat, automatically inflated, shot toward the opening above the pilot's seat, carrying Ken with it into the free air above the waves.

CHAPTER 2

ADRIFT IN THE CORAL SEA

Save the medicine! Save the medicine! The words pounded in Ken's mind as he shot to the surface. He lost all sense of time and space, knowing only that above him was the free air.

The rope from the rubber boat was tangled around his right wrist and he was being kept miraculously afloat. How long he was in that state of semideadness he had no way of telling. But suddenly, like the burst of a shell, a loud noise roared through his ears and he felt himself being dragged below the waves. Although he fought the water with all his strength, the suction pulled him down.

His mind cleared and he prayed for deliverance, realizing that he had been caught in the undertow of the sinking bomber.

The waters shall not overflow thee. The Scripture promise brought courage, and in that moment he knew deliverance would come. In his fingers he felt the lifeboat rope and he was soon being pulled to the surface.

The bomber bobbed like a cork on the waters. Ken looked about him, and he could see only the twenty-to-forty-foot waves pounding ceaselessly one against the other. The last to leave the wounded bomber, he thought that all the others who had escaped must have floated clear and been carried beyond sight by the waves.

He felt alone, yet not alone, for he was conscious of the presence of Christ who long ago had mastered the waves. *Lo, I am with you alway, even unto the end . . .* It was as if Jesus had spoken those words to him. A prayer of thanksgiving sprang to his lips—and then he recalled the lost package.

I have betrayed a trust, he thought, remembering the package he had given to Cory. Scanning the waves, he thought he saw something afloat, but knew this could not be, unless one of the other rubber boats had been washed back in sight.

Looking again, he saw that something was riding the crest of a high wave, and was being propelled toward the boat which was sustaining him.

"It can't be," he said aloud, "but it is," he continued as he realized that the floating package contained the miracle drug.

The package was beyond his reach, and he knew it would be foolishly bold to loose the raft's rope so that he might swim to the package. There was only one thing to do: he must plunge into the water, tow the raft to the package, and then rescue the precious drug.

His arms were sinewy. As a nine-year-old boy he had learned how to rope cattle, and for many years he had managed several hundred animals. He recalled the many times he had swum in the Colorado River as it cut its way a mile below the top of the Grand Canyon. With a one-armed breast stroke he struck out for the package, still atop a wave.

Although he fought the waters with all his strength, he could make no progress toward the package. He prayed to God for strength, but still the waves made it impossible for him to reach the drifting drug.

I wasn't using my head, he thought as he remembered the aluminum oars which were stowed in the tiny raft.

Turning toward the rubber craft, he saw that it was upside down, and pulling himself beside it, he fought the waters in an attempt to right the float. Just as he got the craft on its end, a wave flapped it upside down again.

Fighting the water, he tried to play shark with the upturned boat, and diving underneath, he came up directly below the craft, and with both arms gave it a sidewise push, praying the while that God would undertake for him.

"Thank God!" he shouted as the boat landed right side up.

He knew his battle was not over, for in his dive he had lost hold of the rope and the boat floated clear on the next wave. He was now loose; thousands of miles of water separated him from the nearest land. If he did not make the boat, he could live but ten more hours.

He remembered having heard the bomber's crew speak of the length of time a man could remain afloat in water; about the length of time between suns, they decided. It was do or die. Sighting the location of the boat, Ken lowered his head, and in a powerful crawl pushed toward the spot where he prayed the boat might be.

Something brushed by—long, slimy—and he felt a fin graze the flesh of his forearm.

The full force of that graze struck him.

Man-eating shark! he thought, recalling that the captain had said just before the bomber crashed that sharks were plentiful in these South Pacific waters. As he fought the waves, his hand struck something that responded to his touch, and coming to the surface, he found the rubber boat directly in front of him.

By the time he had pulled himself over the slippery edge, he was exhausted, and he lay back, his head against one end of the raft and his legs athwart the other. He wanted to stay there and rest, and fall into a semiconscious sleep.

The word began pounding in his brain again . . . *penicillin* . . . *penicillin.* He could see long rows of hospital cots, and on them young American boys, calling, clamoring, *"The medicine, the medicine."*

As thy days, so shall thy strength be.

The Bible promise came clearly to his mind, and he felt strength flow back into his exhausted arms, sweep to his stalwart limbs, surge through his body. He sat up; searched for the oars; found them; touched them overside to the waters; turned his gaze to the waves' tops; hunted the troughs of the waves; searched, looked, scanned, prayed, believed. Out there, riding a crest which curled in the wind, was a bobbing package!

"It is waterproof." He could hear the general say these words in the White House room where he had received his charge thirty-two hours before.

"Thank God," he breathed as he watched the package which meant life to thousands of infected boys, who otherwise would be doomed to die from the dreaded *staphylococcus aures,* a virulent type of blood poisoning. Ken remembered having heard Dr. Kenedy and the pilot discuss another rare form of death-dealing *staphylococcus hemolytious septicemi*, from which some of the men had suffered. *Terrible sounding, and worse to have,* Ken thought.

"In every case where the sulpha drugs have failed, penicillin has brought about a recovery," the major had said.

Only a wave's length away floated the precious package! In Ken's hands were two small aluminum oars, and he rode a rubber boat. The treacherous waters pounded on every side. He prayed for strength—strength to fight the waves, to ride down the slough and then climb to the crest of the wave nearest his.

With a will to do, he set his shoulders to the task, saying, "A charge to keep I have, a God to glorify . . ."

As he pulled, he felt new strength flow through his arms, and although a moment before he had been too weak even to sit up, now he fought the waves with unconquerable energy. He realized that other hands had been placed over his, and they supplied the energy to row the boat slowly down the trough of one wave and up the crest of another.

He crept closer to the package, still nearer, and when he was close enough to reach it, he slackened his right oar, pulled the tiny thing into the boat, and then grasped the handle which had been placed on the package.

At that instant something grazed the bottom of his boat and shook it sidewise until Ken thought it would be upset. He saw the loosened oar topple overboard and plummet to the bottom, as the package bobbed away.

He wanted to cry. Instead he prayed for new strength to conquer the waters which fought against him.

"God," he prayed, "walk on these waves to me, that I might be strong enough to rescue the medicine."

The verse of a song came to his lips and he sang, "Lord, I believe; Lord, I believe. Saviour, raise my faith in Thee till it can move a mountain."

For an instant the waves subsided, the waters became still, and the package floated within reach as if propelled by a divine hand. Pulling it into the rubber boat, Ken thanked God for returning the precious package to him.

At that moment he remembered the crash. It had happened so swiftly that he had lost all sense of continuity. He knew that his good friend Major Jim Kenedy, whom he loved to call Dr. Jim, was dead. Ken was glad the doctor had gone down with the bomber and had not been left to drift on the waves and be devoured by the fierce sharks. The lad, serious for his age, tried to figure out how the penicillin had been left to float, but when he recalled having looked out of the bomber as Cory had roused him from the daze caused by the landing, he remembered having seen two other men struggling with a life raft, and he knew that when Cory joined them there was little room left for the penicillin.

Looking at the sky for the first time, he noticed that the sun was slipping over the horizon. He had lost all sense of time and since the crash had occurred before midmorning, Ken knew that what to him had seemed a short struggle had in reality taken the major part of the day.

In the region of his stomach was a gnawing which did not require an expert scientist to classify as hunger, and he said, "I'm hungry enough to eat the toenails off a bobcat, and I shore wish I could hear Uncle Les' colored cook Sambo sing out, 'Come and git hit afore I throws hit out.'"

Ken had little equipment. True, he had an aluminum oar with which, so he thought, he might "catch" a fish. Searching in the storage compartments, he discovered a fishing line and a small package of hooks. As he did so he recalled reading somewhere that after Eddie Rickenbacker, famous flying ace of World War I, had been rescued, someone had started a campaign to equip lifeboats with fish hooks and lines.

He searched, but found no food. Nor was there any "drinking water." He laughed as he looked about him at the waters of the Pacific piled mountain-high everywhere.

"And what's this?" he asked aloud, as he pulled from a small container two rubber bags and a couple of two-inch packages on which were printed the words: FRESH WATER.

Turning the packages over in his hand, he saw that on one side was printed: DIRECTIONS.

He remembered that he had once heard a broadcast in which a scientist described an invention he had made whereby salt water could be purified and turned into water suitable for drinking.

"Thank God," he said, "for science and what it has done, and especially for the divine hand which directs the mind of the scientist."

Here he was in the middle of the Pacific, riding on millions of tons of food, and in his hands were the chemicals by which fresh water could be taken out of the briny deep.

As the sun sank in the west, his face felt burned, and he was surprised that the sun, reflected by the water, should so soon scorch, crack and parch his skin, accustomed as he was to the winds of the West.

A strange sound rose above the crash of the waters, and he strained his ears to listen. At first he thought it was a plane, but soon concluded that his imagination was distorting the sound of the waters so that it resembled the rhythmic pounding of an airplane.

The sound grew louder. Scanning the heavens, Ken saw a plane riding low, about a quarter of a mile away, he estimated. Standing, he began to wave and shout frantically, knowing that rescue was near.

Suddenly two jets of fire burst from the plane's snout. He could see it as the plane skipped over the waters. Then he heard guns bursting, and he saw on a wing the emblem of the Rising Sun.

Like a stone he dropped to the raft, crawled between the outer rolled edges, and pushed his body down into the tough rubber bottom as if to hide himself in the craft.

His hand touched his pocket and there he felt the familiar lump made by his New Testament. He thanked God that he had not lost this precious treasure, for it was a waterproof one given him by a friend. He heard the Master speak above the roar from the plane's machine guns: *Men ought always to pray, and not to faint.*

At first he had been frightened when he recognized the Japanese plane, which doubtless had strafed the other three lifeboats that were hidden behind the towering mountains of water; now the assurance of Christ's presence came to him. He felt divinely appointed to this mission of mercy.

He believed that he would "come through" alive with the penicillin, that those boys who were willing to die for their country might become well. He had a strong affection for them already, and he longed to read to them, one by one, from his New Testament to which the Psalms had been added, the wonderful words of life.

"Deliver me now, while I call upon Thee, dear Lord, that I might live for this mission and see it through. Bless those sick and wounded boys over in Australia," he prayed. Then he added earnestly, "Don't let the pilot see me . . ."

The plane winged low, veered to the right, zoomed high overhead, as if searching the waters for evidence of life. Then the pilot made a power dive, and when just above the water, he leveled off, and Ken could see the line of fire spouting from the guns' muzzles. A stream of tracer bullets streaked into the water.

Ken knew the pilot had come back to make sure that this mercy errand would never be completed. A wicked ruler and his organization of military men had poisoned their bullets, which had filled the American boys' bodies with the most deadly of germs, and when the cruel oppressors knew the life-giving medicine was on its way to heal the suffering Americans, a spy ring in America had sent forward the news of the bomber's flight.

All this unraveled in Ken's thinking as darkness covered the Pacific.

The secret of the mercy flight had been discovered, and espionage agents had followed the plane to Hickam Field, where another spy agent had sabotaged the navigation instruments so that the plane would fly a course to a section of the Pacific in control of the enemy.

Ken said to himself as the heat of day turned to the icy chill of night, "Those frantic messages the radioman sent out were intercepted by the Japanese, who sent the plane to make sure we were done for."

The night was clear, and the sky was bright with stars. Ken turned over in his mind a passage which his mother had taught him before her death:

The eyes of the Lord are over the righteous, and his ears are open to their prayers.

The night winds whipped the ocean into a frenzy of spray; but Ken was sure that the Lord noted his position, and though he might be many miles from island or land, he was safe under divine protection.

CHAPTER 3

ALONE ON THE SOUTH SEAS

The heavens declare the glory of God; and the firmament sheweth his handywork.

Ken, drifting on the South Seas, saw the millions of stars, and he remembered the words of David, which he had often quoted at night when he lived on the Painted Desert. Tonight as the waves rocked the tiny rubber boat, which on the inside was about eighteen inches wide and three feet long, Ken lifted his voice in thanksgiving to God for delivering him from the bomber.

He placed the package of drugs in one end of the raft and seated himself with his back to the other end, which made it necessary for his feet to rest on the top of the package and hang over the outer edge of the boat. The day had been hot, and the sun reflected by the water burned like a torch. When night came, the winds whipped the waves and showered him with a fine, chilling spray.

"Whew!" he whistled. "Wish I had my leather jacket; but that went overboard with all my spare clothes," he said aloud, knowing that no one was near enough to hear his words.

His parched mouth, briny with the salt spray, clamored for water, and he remembered the package marked FRESH WATER. He could not recall how the scientist had said to use the package, and he wished for a flashlight. He remembered that he had thrown his spare flashlight out of the bomber. "Wow! How foolish to pull a stunt like that. My Pacific kingdom"—he swept his arms toward the waters—"for a flash—"

The words were torn from his lips. The rubber raft was raised clear of the water and hurled into the air. Ken, grabbing the outer roll of the boat, which was about twice the size of an automobile inner tube, rode it as if it were a bucking bronco on the Arizona Bar-H.

"Ride 'er, cowboy!" he yelled, but without glee.

Then the boat settled on a wave's hump and started to do a series of half-turns, as if some mysterious hand were turning it.

In the dim light of the moon, which by this time had burst full and clear upon the horizon, Ken saw a black fin cut the water and a long slippery back tear the waves in a ripple. Beside it floated another slippery back, and Ken's flesh began to crawl as if he had sat down on a desert ant bed.

"Man-eaters!"

Ken's words faltered. Fear struck him and he lifted his hands free of the boat's outer edges. In the jostle he had been thrown across the boat, so that his legs hung over the edge and dripped into the water. Instantly a shark whirled by and ripped the leg of his trousers to the knee.

Jerking his legs out of the water, Ken could see through the rip a thin line of red on his flesh.

Memory played a cruel trick on him. He remembered a conversation he had heard between Rick, the radioman, and Major Jim, when the doctor had said, "They tell me that when a man-eater gets a taste of blood, he goes hog-wild." "Believe me, Major, you're right on that. I spent ten days on a raft after being shot out of the skies, when there was plenty of bleeding, and those sharks did their best to get at us," was Rick's reply.

Ken's mind played weird tricks on him. He even believed that the man-eater would swamp the boat to get another taste of his red blood.

Ken prayed for an island to burst upon the midnight horizon. None came, but he felt the edge of the package cutting into the calves of his legs, and then he was sure God would see him through.

"I must make it," he said aloud, hoping that his words would drive away the fears that he would fail, "and by the grace of God I will."

His eyes became heavy, but as the man-eating sharks continued to brush against the boat's bottom, jabbing fins into it, he knew there must be no sleep for him that night.

The stars suddenly faded, and overhead where the moon was riding, a darkness appeared, which gradually became inky blackness as the heavens were blotted out by a thick cloud. Shortly, without warning, the clouds broke in a deluge such as is possible only in the tropics.

"Cold . . . drenchy . . ." he said. He felt the salt being washed from his body, face and lips, and the mouthful of sweet water which he swallowed burned like a white-hot coal.

The rain disappeared as suddenly as it had come, and the sleepy boy found himself fully refreshed by the water he had found in the bottom of the boat.

Although a mere boy, Ken faced hardships which would tax the nerve and faith of even a full-grown man. He sensed, however, that his mission was important enough to cause Uncle Sam to send his finest bomber crew and one of the best-trained doctors halfway around the world.

"Here I am, just fourteen, and charged with what the whole crew and Dr. Jim had to carry through," he said to himself, yet not to himself, for in that moment his voice lifted in a prayer, thanking God for the water and asking for aid: ". . . Lord, I must not fail, and under Thy protecting care I cannot. Whatever else I do in life, help me to do this one thing well. And remember those suffering boys."

His eyes rolled shut, and the rocking of the rubber boat and the tossing of the waves lulled him to sleep. He had flown thirty-two hours from the mainland starting point, and had stopped for only two hours at Hickam Field. Ken's mind and body could no longer endure the strain. He had

had very little sleep—cat-naps as the sky bomber shot through the heavens on its mercy errand.

The wind rocked the waves, and Ken found himself being thrown out of the raft. Half dazed, he lost his balance and went down and down. He felt as if he would never stop going down. He knew he had changed directions, if not ends, and was being hurled again to the surface. The Mae West was tight against his neck.

Water spurted from his mouth. Fighting the water with his hands until he was fully awake, he began to pray for direction and aid. Fortunately he had worn his Mae West jacket during the day and night "boat ride," and this kept him afloat, jabbing his chin and trouncing the back of his head.

Like a bursting bomb this thought hurled itself at him out of the dark night: *I have failed my country.*

Ken knew the salt of his tears was mingling with the salt of the South Seas, and he was not ashamed, for he had broken faith with the general, the President, a hundred and thirty million countrymen, and especially the ten thousand hospitalized boys who were clamoring for the penicillin.

Scanning the dark ocean, Ken could see nothing but waves towering above, crashing over him, booming through the gloom.

Until now he had been encouraged by an undaunted faith that he would "make it through" with the penicillin. This hope for the first time left him and vanished in the misty night.

He turned his thoughts to the ten hours or thereabouts during which his Mae West would keep him afloat, and beyond that he could not think.

Starting to swim, he fought the waters slapdash. Hurrying to nowhere in particular, he rushed to get there as soon as possible. Then he realized the futility and uselessness of it all. He slowed his legs to a dead stop; threshed no more with his arms; tried to face the end.

I will proceed to do a marvellous work among this people, even a . . . wonder.

Ken could not remember where he had read or heard this passage, nor was he sure it was from the Bible, but like a burst from a machine gun it rattled its way into his brain.

Speak, Lord; for thy servant heareth.

Recalling these words from young Samuel's life, when God wanted to deliver a message to him, the floating boy gave himself to the tide, riding the waves as they dipped and lashed, breathing a prayer that the magic drug might somehow be brought to shore.

He must have slept, for he felt himself being pounded, threshed back and forth against something stony. Rousing himself, he reached out a hand and it struck a rocky projection. Prying his eyes open, he looked out. The sky was radiant with a purple glow, and turning, he saw in the distance what appeared to be a thin thread of palm trees silhouetted against the skyline.

He could not believe his eyes, and said aloud, "Must be a South Sea mirage. Pshaw, I've seen better mirages on the plains of Arizona, whole towns and water and lakes and cattle."

His mind would not rouse itself. He had been pounded by the surf and tossed against the coral reef for he knew not how long. But when he gained full consciousness, there it was not a hundred yards away—a palm-lined island. How big it was he could not tell, but he was sure that it was big enough for him to lie down and sleep for a week.

God had worked the wonder. Ken was sure of it. At that moment he saw a young native come from between two palm trees, carrying something water-soaked and square.

Could it be the precious drug? His mission to fulfill for his country?

At that distance he could not tell, but he thought:

When I fell out of the boat the penicillin package was also thrown clear, and as I drifted, it was carried by the same current, so we both stayed pretty close together. Wonder where the raft is.

Scanning the reef which barred his way to the island, Ken could see nothing that resembled the torn remains of a lifeboat. Looking to where the island made a bend or curved out of sight, he was surprised to see a native walking on the sands, carrying over his head something shaped like a canoe.

No, it can't be a canoe, Ken thought, *but maybe it is a banana leaf turned over his head.*

"*Wow!*" he yelled. "It's the rubber boat!"

The native, who had come from among the palm trees in response to Ken's shout, rushed toward the water, and throwing himself into the surf, swam with powerful strokes through the breakers. Ken watched the swimmer cut through the waves as they curled over him and boiled upward from the sands.

The reef behind which the boy was standing was being pounded mercilessly, and the waters broke in a ten-foot wall of spray. Ken could not see the swimmer distinctly. He could see only an occasional flash of brown flesh and a black head cutting through the water.

The swimmer came nearer, and then with a powerful stroke shot through the last wall of water and slowly climbed over the coral reef.

"A girl," Ken said. The native girl answered, "Howdy. You American?"

"And how," returned the boy, surprised that the South Sea Island girl could talk "good ole American."

The girl, dripping wet, smiled and showed the whitest

teeth Ken had ever seen. She threw her head back and her long black hair waved in the wind. She was fully clothed in her native dress. As Ken smiled back at her, he thought how beautiful she was.

"Where did you learn to speak American?" he asked, somewhat embarrassed at the situation in which he found himself.

"Missionaries lived on our island until the Japs came, and I learned their language in the missionary school," returned the girl, reaching out her hand toward Ken, who was in water above his head.

Gripping her hand tightly, the lad was able to pull himself over the reef, and standing up on it, he looked toward the island, where he saw a boy somewhat older than himself carrying the rubber raft on his head.

"My brother," said the native girl. "We come here to gather coconuts. Since the Japanese took our island and killed our parents, my brother and I hide out all the time, and live wherever we can."

Ken noticed that the girl spoke fair English with a trace of native accent. He thought she was about five-feet-four and weighed nearly one hundred and fifteen pounds. Her limbs were brown, and she was barefooted. Her hands were small and her arms were long and perfectly shaped.

"Where you from? You're not a flier, are you, like so many that have come to our island?" she asked.

"Nope, not a flier. Just an American boy, fourteen, and rarin' to git to Australia. Know where it is from here?"

"Sure, over there," she said, pointing toward what Ken thought was south.

"How on earth did I drift this way?" he asked more of himself than the girl. "The bomber I was on was flying from Honolulu to Australia and we were wrecked, and I haven't any idea where we went down."

"This island is in the Gulf of Papua, and that way is New Guinea."

"So that's where all that fighting is going on and where General MacArthur is . . ."

The girl shook her head as if to say she knew nothing about the general or the fighting. "The Japs, they came, took our island, killed our people, captured the missionaries, and my brother—his name is Ron—and I, we escaped and we go every island," she explained, sweeping her hands in a wide circle to indicate that their home was wherever night found them.

"I guess it's proper like," Ken began, lifting the Mae West vest over his head, "seein' you're a missionary-taught South Sea Islander, to introduce myself. I'm Ken Murray of the Bar-H Ranch in Arizona."

"Rancho grande," the girl said. "Our missionary told us about your country and the big, big country and—how do you say it?—the cows?"

Ken laughed at the girl's search for words to express her delight at coming face to face with someone from the faraway land which was the home of her missionary friends.

While they talked Ken saw the native boy Ron dive into the water and with long strokes fight through the breakers to where Ken and the native girl were.

"And I am," the girl said hesitatingly, "Tamara. My mother she gave me the name."

The boy, grinning, cut through the last breaker and swam to the reef, saying plainly, "I find—how do you say it?—your boat."

"And say, did you find anything else?"

"Little package, like this?" asked the girl, holding her hands about a foot apart.

"Shore, that's her. It's the . . ." Then he thought about the pricelessness of that package.

CHAPTER 4

LIVING ON A CORAL ISLAND

"You big fren," said Ron, the island boy, to Ken, as he reached out a hand to the rescued lad. "Live with us now," he continued, sweeping his hands over the island as an indication that this was to be his new home.

"Nope, can't stay here. Gotta get on to Australia. I promised," said Ken, and at the moment Tamara began to speak rapidly to her brother. Although she spoke in her native tongue, Ken caught the word "Australia" and saw the boy shake his head at the mention of it.

"No can do," said the native boy. "Heap big boom . . . Japs."

"He can't talk English as well as I can," said the girl, whom Ron had called Tam. "But he means the Japs are liable to fly over here at any time and there would be danger. And besides, our native canoe couldn't make the long water trip."

"Well, anyway, I can try it in my rubber boat. It brought me all this way, and maybe you and Ron can help me make a get-away."

"Me find rubber boat on reef and swim out to get it," said the native.

"And I saw the package which a big wave boomed to the beach," said the girl, lifting her hands to show how the wave washed the penicillin ashore.

Ken looked at his new friends, and decided that they would be faithful to him. There was something about Tam and Ron that made the American boy trust them, so he unburdened his heart.

"This is how it is," he said slowly to Tam, "and you can interpret it to your brother. "That package over there on the beach is worth more than its weight in gold—well, maybe I'd better say coconuts," he added, noticing the palm trees filled with nuts. "It came all the way from America to save the lives of ten thousand soldiers that are about to die in Australia." He hesitated and Tam spoke in her native language, telling her brother with many gestures about Ken's package. When she had finished the cowboy continued:

"And I've just gotta git it to those soldiers that the Japs poisoned . . ."

At the word "Jap," Ron shook his fist toward the sky, as if to say to Ken that they were his enemies, too.

"So you know what they have done to your folks, Tam?" asked Ken. The girl nodded. "They kill Mamma and Papa," said Ron, wiping a tear from his eyes. Tam moved over on the reef and put her arms around her brother.

Ron offered his hand and said, "We blood brothers. We fight. We help fren git to faraway land."

"He means Australia," said Tam.

"Come, let's go to island," continued Ron, as he stepped into the water and motioned for the others to follow.

Until that moment Ken had not known how utterly exhausted he was. As he started to rise—he had been seated on the coral reef—his legs buckled under him and he fell. Ron, leaping to his side, lifted him; Tam took hold of one arm, and together they steadied the lad.

"Maybe I'd better put this Mae West on," Ken said, reaching for his life jacket.

"Better so," began the powerfully built native boy. "You hold onto me, and I bring you in." He stepped into the water and placed Ken's hand on his shoulder. Tamara, pointing to her shoulder, said, "Put other hand here."

Together the three touched the water, which for the moment was calm, and the two natives began to swim toward the shore. Ken held onto them. When they hit the first breaker, Tam told Ken to hold his breath, and swiftly the brother and sister plunged into the waves, pulling Ken with them.

Those hundred yards were the longest Ken had ever gone, and had it not been for his new friends, exhausted as he was, he would have had to remain on the reef. He felt the powerful one-arm strokes of Tam and Ron as they swam through the breakers with an ease which came from many hours spent in the water.

When Tam and Ron were able to touch the sands, they lifted Ken to his feet, but he fell to the ground. Placing their arms around Ken's taut body, they made their way to the beach, where they gently laid the lad on the sand. Ken lay still for a moment, breathing with difficulty, and Tam began to rub his limbs with long sweeping movements of her hands.

"This way we bring you back strength," she said, smiling at the prone lad. Ron began to massage Ken's arms, and then turned him on his back. The Arizona boy could feel their warm, tender hands rubbing strength into his muscles. Soon he sat up, drew his knees under him, and then knelt.

"I want to thank God for sending me such fine friends," Ken began, "and I want you to kneel with me here on the sand, so I can pray. You know how to pray?" he asked, looking at Tam, and then at her brother.

"I know. I belong Jesus," said the bronze-skinned girl, falling on her knees by Ken's side.

"What about you, Ron? You love Jesus?"

The native lad was silent, refusing to speak, as if he did not understand what the American meant. Then Tamara said, "He is not Jesus' boy. When the Japs kill our parents and capture our missionaries, Ron he did not like it, and I can't get him to pray."

Ken looked at his stalwart friend. He had never seen a

more perfect specimen of young manhood. At that moment a great love for Ron swelled in his heart.

"It's like this," Ken began, reaching into his pocket where he kept his New Testament, which in spite of the threshing waves had remained fastened. Opening the zipper (it was a waterproof Testament made especially by the American Bible Society for the use of sailors and soldiers), Ken said:

"It's this way, Ron. Like the missionary said"—at that moment Ken felt thankful that he could in a small way be a missionary for his Master—"if you let Jesus come into your heart He will save you and always be your Friend. You can pray to Him and He will answer, and supply all your needs. You must be a Christian to get your prayers answered. And this is the way to be a Christian.

"First, you must confess your sins, for the Bible says, *If we confess our sins, he is faithful and just to forgive us our sins.* Why don't you kneel here right now and let Jesus save you?"

Ron's sister took him by the hand and said, "This is what the missionary told us, and Ron, won't you be Jesus' boy?" Then she spoke in her native language, which Ken did not understand, but he felt the warmth of her heart, and he knew that as a Christian she was pleading with her brother.

Opening the Testament, Ken read:

For God so loved the world, that he gave his only begotten Son, that whosoever believeth in him should not perish, but have everlasting life. And, *He that believeth on the Son hath everlasting life.* Turning the pages again to Acts, he read, *Repent, and be baptized every one of you in the name of Jesus Christ for the remission of sins, and ye shall receive the gift of the Holy Ghost.*

Cast away from you all your transgressions, whereby ye have transgressed; and make you a new heart and a new spirit . . . A new heart also will I give you, and a new spirit will I put within you: and I will take away the stony heart

*out of your flesh, and I will give you an heart of flesh. And
I will put my spirit within you, and cause you to walk in my
statutes.*

The last verses he quoted from memory, and then reached
over to the native boy, who looked steadfastly at him. "Let's
kneel, Ron, and let Jesus forgive your sins, and then you can
be baptized."

Ron fell to his knees, and while Tamara prayed in her
native tongue, Ken called upon Jesus to save the lad, saying:

"Lord, Ron, this boy, who is all alone with his sister here
on this island, is coming to Thee. He wants to be saved. He
needs Thy friendship. Come into his heart right now as he
prays and make him clean within. Forgive his sins and
teach him to trust in Thee. Amen."

Turning to the praying native, he said, "Ask Jesus to come
into your heart and save you. Confess your sins and believe
that He saves you."

For a moment the boy and his sister prayed in their native
language, and with a smile upon his face, Ron said, "I'm
Jesus' boy. It's good in here," he exclaimed, touching his
heart.

"Thank God," said Ken, grateful that once more he had
been able to lead another soul to Christ. "What do we eat?"
he asked suddenly, remembering how long his stomach had
seemed to be sticking to his backbone. "I believe I could
eat a coconut—shell, or hull or whatever you call it, and all."

Tamara raced to a near-by palm tree, and picked up a nut
from the ground. She carried it to her brother, who took the
nut to a jagged piece of coral reef which was just above the
water's edge, and broke it open.

Coming back to Ken, he offered the broken nut to him,
saying, "Heap good coconut milk. Drink."

Ken took the bowl-like nut and drank the milk, a whitish
substance, which at least helped to satisfy his thirst. Ron

meanwhile drew a knife from his sheath and began to scrape off the soft meat. Then he handed the cracked nut to the Arizona lad.

"It's good to eat," said Tamara, to which Ron added, "Make you strong," as he flexed his muscles and pinched Ken's leg through the rent in his trousers which the shark's fin had made.

Ken could not forget his unfinished mission. He had been given a charge to finish this task, and somehow, despite the difficulties which at the moment seemed beyond his power to measure or understand, he knew that he must go on.

"Well, here we are, and how do we go from here to Australia?" he asked.

Tamara shook her head, and Ken noticed that the long hair, which fell in wet ringlets to her shoulders, shone brilliantly in the sun. It was jet-black and curly. At that moment he realized the girl was as beautiful as any he had ever seen, and he wished that somehow he might take her and Ron back to the Bar-H Ranch with him.

Ron, however, sat with a finger on his forehead as if working out a plan. Then, slapping his head as if to bring the plan to the surface, he said:

"Heap big Jap boats on next island." He pointed toward the west. "Maybe so tonight, we steal one, and go to faraway land."

Tamara gave a surprised *ooo-oooh!* Ron interrupted. "No can do. Can't make it go boom-boom-boom."

Ken caught his meaning and said, "You mean you don't know how to run the engine?"

The native nodded his head quickly, and Ken said, "Maybe I can run the motor. I know how to fly an airplane a little, and drive a car, and on the ranch we have gas engines."

Together they decided that when the moon went down they would take the native canoe and row across to the neighboring island, on which was a small patrol of Japanese soldiers. When their plans were made, Ken had an opportunity to take a good look at the island on which he had been cast.

All about him were palm trees, filled with coconuts. He saw many native fruits hanging from trees, and wild flowers in abundance.

He exclaimed, "Why, this is like Paradise itself. You ought to be glad, Tam, to live on such an island as this. Why, you've got your food hanging everywhere and livin' oughtn't to be any problem at all." Ken cut his sentence short and his eyes bulged as he saw a large crocodile swim lazily down a small stream which ran into the ocean.

"Wow!" he shouted, grabbing Ron by one arm and Tam by the other, "let's high-tail out of here. That thing—why, it would swallow us alive!"

The natives shied away from the crocodile, but Ron smiled and Tam broke into a low-pitched musical laugh. To them the sight of a crocodile was not at all strange. They had spent their lives among such animals.

"I almost forgot," said Ken, recalling the penicillin. "Where did you put the package?"

Tam walked gracefully toward a small enclosure made by a group of palms. Ken noticed her as she pushed back the low fronds and went into what seemed to be a room. He yielded to his curiosity and walked toward the enclosure, which was a large roomlike space, completely covered by a heavy curtain of palm leaves. In one corner he saw a few bundles, and beside them the precious cargo for which he was willing to give his life.

"Here it is," said Tam, handing the medicine to him.

"So this is where you live?" he asked.

"Yes, Ken, our American friend, this is how we live since the Japs drove us out of our home island. They burned our home, and this is all we have left," said Tam, sweeping her hand toward the bundles.

Ken had all he could do to keep back tears of sorrow at the sad plight of Tam and her brother. They were South Sea natives, but somehow they seemed as close to him as his own sister Sandra.

"You come home with me to America, Tam, and you can live with us. Uncle Les will be awful glad to have you, and Ron can learn to be a cowboy."

Tamara laughed, recalling the many almost unbelievable stories of America which the missionaries had told.

As the sun began to hide itself behind the island, which Ken and his friends had explored during the afternoon and found to be about a half-mile across, Ron climbed a palm tree and threw down more than two dozen coconuts. As he was coming down the long trunk of the tree, he heard the familiar buzz of an airplane far away, flying at a great speed toward the island.

Ron paused for an instant, cocked his head, and then cried, "Tam, Japs!" Then, frantic with fear, he spoke rapidly in his native tongue. Meanwhile he raced down the tree, faster, Ken was sure, than a monkey.

At that moment a monkey in a neighboring tree began to chatter, and was soon joined by a jungle chorus of wild parrots, which flew out of a clump of palms.

"Look at those parrots. Boy, they're sure beautiful. Wish I had one back on the Bar-H."

The plane came closer and the natives pulled Ken deep into the jungle, lest the enemy pilot should see them.

As the plane came in low over the island, Ken recognized it as a Zero. Huddled on the ground behind palm trees, the young people looked in dread as the ship leveled off just above the treetops. With no warning whatsoever the pilot turned his machine guns on the beach and sprayed the palm trees. At the first burst of fire, Ken plowed into the sand. and Ron screamed, clutching his left shoulder with his right hand.

Ken noticed a streak of red creep from beneath the boy's palm and spread down his arm.

"You're hit," said Ken, as Tamara screamed something in her native language.

Immediately Ken thought of the penicillin, and for a moment he considered opening the package and using the drug.

"Let me look at it, Ron," said Ken, who was no stranger to wounds, for many times he had watched his mother and, later, Les Lee, owner of the Bar-H, treat wounded men and animals. "Get me a cloth, Tam, so I can wipe the blood off."

"This is all I have," the girl said, holding her skirt. Then Ken realized that the girl wore all the clothes she possessed, as did also the boy. Reaching into his pocket, Ken took out one of the now wet handkerchiefs he had retrieved from his luggage just before throwing it into the ocean.

Slowly he wiped the blood from the wound, which he found to be a round hole as large as his thumb in the center of the boy's shoulder.

"Musta broke your shoulder," he said. "Tam, I guess we'd better wash it out with clean water and then make a salt-water pack over it."

Lifting his face to the heavens, Ken prayed:

"Dear Lord, here we are a long ways from where I must go, and Ron has been shot, and I pray Thee to help us right now. Don't let the fever set in, and keep blood poisoning away, and heal Ron for Jesus' sake. Help me to get this medicine to Australia and take care of us until we land safely there. For Jesus' sake. Amen."

CHAPTER 5

FINDING THE WALKIE-TALKIE

"Australia is a long ways off," Ken said to Tamara, as she began to cut the heavy string which bound the package. "And I'll never make it unless you and Ron help me. If Ron's arm doesn't get well that means he won't be able to go along, and you and I could never undertake such a trip."

Tam shook her head, and Ken could see her bite deep into her lower lip, until the blood seemed to be pushed out of it. She felt helpless in spite of the fact that she had lived in tropical jungles all her life, for she realized that unless her brother recovered she would be totally at the mercy of the wilds.

Not for anything would Ken have betrayed the sacred trust of delivering the precious drug to the soldiers, but in the present emergency he felt that without Ron he would be unable to make the sea trip. With a prayer on his lips, he cut into the package, carefully, as if expecting at any moment to destroy the life-giving medicine.

He found several small tins, securely wrapped against moisture, with no writing or printing on them. Then gradually he came nearer to the bottom of the package, and at last found what he was looking for: a tiny tube with a syringe head, about which he had heard Major Kenedy tell. On the trip to Hickam Field the doctor had said:

"We are trying to work out a field pack which a wounded soldier can administer himself. It's something like the tubes of morphine the soldiers carry. When they are wounded all they have to do is to jab the syringe needle into their arm and then give the tube a squeeze."

Ken recognized the small syringe tubes, and though he was brave enough in most situations calling for nerve, when he thought of using one of these tiny tubes of precious medicine, he faltered. Looking at Tam, he saw that her face was pasty white, and Ron had fallen to the sand.

"Do you suppose," he began, hesitating to put the awful thought into words, "that the Japs have poi—" He could not go on.

Tam, her eyes wide open, looked with horror at the American as she, too, caught his meaning. Ron was silent, breathing slowly, and Ken saw that he was unconscious.

"Poisoned . . ."

This took all fear out of Ken, for here in the presence of death, with the precious drug in his hands and the Heavenly Father above, he could not hesitate.

"Let's pray, Ken," said Tam. She, too, knew what they faced. In her native tongue she began to call upon God. Her eyes were closed and her hands were lifted toward the skies. While Ken was praying silently, the South Sea Island girl concluded her prayer in English:

"Don't let him die. He is all I have in this world. They took my missionary, killed my papa and mamma, and here we are all alone. Help Ken right now as he uses this medicine. Amen."

Taking the tiny syringe (the tube and syringe needle were less than two inches long), Ken reached for Ron's bare arm. Wishing for alcohol with which to sterilize the skin before jabbing the needle into Ron's arm, Ken pinched the flesh between the forefinger and thumb of his left hand and then placed the needle on the spot, pressing it beneath the surface.

Tam watched with amazement, for though she had been taught in the missionary school, many of the jungle superstitions still clung to her.

"This is the way the doctor said to do it," Ken said, squeezing the tube and forcing the liquid slowly into the boy's arm. "Maybe I ought to have found a vein, for the doc said they sometimes put it into a vein, and sometimes in a muscle, and they have some that you take by your mouth." Ken explained to the girl all he remembered of the army doctor's conversation concerning the drug and its results.

"This penicillin is awfully hard to make. It comes from a mold, like mold on bread. As the mold grows on top of the bottles where they put a solution of mineral salts and sugar, a fluid secretes from the mold, and this is drained off. Shore hard, the doc said, to get the stuff. And there ain't much of it in the world, but they are working on it hard. The government is spending millions of dollars to produce the stuff."

"Will it save Ron's life?" asked Tamara, trying to understand what Ken was saying about the drug.

"Shore hope so. Most powerful medicine in the world, the army doctor said. Kills germs and bacteria quicker than anything that has ever been found."

Ken knew that all he could do was to follow the directions printed on the tubes and leave the lad in God's hands. During the afternoon he and Tam kept a close watch over the boy, whom they had placed on a bed made of banana leaves and other jungle growth. Ron did not regain consciousness, but lay prone on his jungle bed, breathing slowly

At sundown Ken gave him another injection of penicillin, praying meanwhile that the miracle drug might rouse the boy to consciousness. Ron's shoulder seemed to be shattered, and Ken prayed that he might bind it properly, so that it would mend as soon as possible.

"The boat, Ken. We'd better go?"

"What, Tam? You mean you are willing to risk your life and leave Ron here alone just to help me steal a boat from the Japs to get this penicillin to Australia?"

"They need it over there, those brave soldiers who fight so hard to give us our island back again. We be back here in one-two hours after moondown."

Ken recalled the full moon of the previous nights and said, "But it's full moon and we wouldn't dare be sleuthing around the patrol with so much light."

"Pretty soon," said the girl, "come a heavy fog. I feel it, and maybe so rain, and then we won't be seen."

"You mean most every night there is a fog?"

Tamara shook her head, saying, "Hot in daytime and night wind bring fog."

After waiting for hours, Ken felt the dampness of the fog, and Tam said, "Let's go now and hurry back."

Slipping out of the palm-lined opening to which they had carried the injured lad, Tam made her way to a small jungle-covered cove, Ken following her. "Here it is," said the girl, as Ken felt the rough edge of a native dugout strike his shin. "We push it out into the waves."

"But the reef?" asked the lad, recalling his experience with the waves that lashed the coral around the island.

"I know an opening and the tide goes out through it now. No trouble that way. We make it sure, and Jesus will help us."

Slowly they pushed the dugout into the water, and when the water was of sufficient depth, Tam and Ken climbed in. Tam handed Ken a paddle. He felt the swift current as it swept through the reef's opening, and in a short time they were drifting toward the open sea.

"The current it go this way by the big island where the Japs are and we won't have to do any paddling. Just guide the canoe."

Ken felt the dugout, which had been hollowed from a native tree, being propelled swiftly, racing, it seemed to Ken, at a speed of more than ten knots an hour. The girl was quiet, and Ken held his breath, for at any moment a patrol boat, its guns blazing, might slip out of the fog.

After about an hour, as Ken estimated the time, Tam said, "We're there," and Ken felt the dugout scrape the beach. It was after midnight, and Tam, knowing the location of the patrol's headquarters, skirted it, not wanting to run into a trap. Carefully the two climbed out of the dugout and slowly made their way along the water's edge to the place where the enemy boats had last been seen by Tam and her brother.

"Boats," Tam whispered in Ken's ear, and the lad saw dim forms of what he thought were landing barges. Having seen similar barges in action at Hickam Field, he knew that such a craft would be too cumbersome for their needs, so they sought further for a light patrol or speed boat. Finally they found a lightweight motor launch, into which Ken climbed.

"This is it," he said to Tam, who had followed him aboard. He inspected it carefully, locating the engine, becoming acquainted with its steering wheel. Then his fingers touched something about which he had not thought.

"Radio," he said in a low voice, "and it's portable." He had discovered a Japanese version of the popular American army walkie-talkie, a portable sending-receiving set used in scout jeeps, and carried even by soldiers in combat. He thanked God for this discovery, knowing there were limitless possibilities for its use.

Finding the rope with which the boat was moored to a makeshift wharf, he loosened it, and with a long oar, which was lying on the bottom of the launch, he poled the boat away from the shore.

Tamara grabbed his arm, and squeezed it, signaling at the same time for silence. In the distance Ken caught the sound of a walking sentry, coming closer. He knew that at a moment's notice a flashlight might burst in his face or blazing searchlights might break upon the fog-bound harbor. Slowly the crunching feet of the Japanese soldier passed by, and Ken breathed easier.

Once the launch was in deeper water, the oar was of no value, and Ken knew he must trust to the tide or current to take him far enough away from the shore so that he could start the motor.

"How far should we be from the shore before starting this thing?" he asked Tam.

"Long ways, Ken, or they might hear us."

Ken argued with himself about the possibility of out-running the Japanese scout boats, and abandoned the idea. He knew that with Ron in a critical condition he could not hope to reach the smaller island, load the penicillin and Ron in the launch and then outdistance the Japs. He asked God for direction and guidance, trusting himself and his island friend to the Father's care. Handing an oar to the island girl, he told her to row with him, and they soon left the enemy-held base.

Suddenly in the distance the blur of a searchlight played upon the fog, and Ken knew the boat had been missed. Thankful for the fog, they rowed on, still afraid to start the motor. Without warning a machine gun opened fire and sprayed the waters around the harbor. Ken watched the deadly stream of fire slowly draw near their boat.

Ken asked aloud, "Dear Lord, deliver us once more, I pray." Tam also voiced a request to the Lord in her own language.

Tam took hold of Ken's arm and drew him slowly down into the boat's bottom. Ken hoped that the bullets would fall short of the boat or that the gunmen would overshoot. He knew the gunner could not see the launch through the fog.

The sound broke with a crash, and the launch seemed to turn around completely as a line of bullets tore a sievelike rent about six inches below the top of the craft. Splinters shot through the air and everything in the boat was thrown helter-skelter, showering Ken and Tam with broken boards, pieces of small instruments, slugs of spent bullets and parts of the motor which had been shot off by the rain of machine gun lead.

When Ken was certain the line of fire was beyond the launch, he lifted his head just over the boat's side and watched the tracer bullets as they made a bright semicircle around the edge of the island.

"We're safe, Tam. Come here. What's the matter?" he asked finally, when she did not answer. Seizing her arm, he tried to lift her, but something held her down. A heavy section of the motor lay across her knees. Ken lifted it from her legs, and then ran his fingers slowly across her face in search of telltale streaks of blood from open wounds.

Finding none, he said aloud, "Thank God, at least she wasn't hit in the head." When he was sure that she had not been hit by a bullet, he reached his cupped hands over the side of the launch, and filling them with water, dashed it in her face.

The girl sighed and said something unintelligible to Ken. He asked, "What is it, Tam? You bad hurt?"

With painful effort the island girl raised herself on an elbow and soon sat up, and brushed her hair from her face.

"What happened?" she asked, her words coming slowly, as if from a great distance

Ken told her about the machine gunning, and Tam, regaining her senses, returned, "Now there is no hope of using the launch, is there?"

Ken said slowly, "Nope . . . guess it was just a pipe dream after all. Hadn't oughta thought I could have made it anyway." The words crept with effort through his half-clenched teeth.

"What was that the missionary used to tell us?" asked Tam, her face close to the lad's. *"All things are possible to him that believeth.* Isn't that the way the Bible says it? God is just as able to help us get the medicine to Australia without a motor or a boat as with them. Don't you believe?"

Tam's faith in God's ability to help them strengthened

Ken's faltering trust that he would accomplish the task given him to fulfill, and he said, "We'll make it under God—you and I and Ron."

Ken knew that in the morning the launch must be found in a shattered condition by the Japs, or else they would send out a party to search every nook and corner of each island, however tiny, until the three of them were discovered. On the other hand, if in the morning the launch was discovered by the patrol boat or a searching plane and was drifting idly on the ocean, they might think that the boat broke its moorings, and the search would be abandoned.

"How far to the island where Ron is, Tam?"

"Maybe so two hours' swim," she returned. "You thinking what I'm thinking—that we ought to swim on to the island and leave the boat here?"

"You hit her right on the nose, gal," said Ken. Tam's tinkling laugh answered the boy's friendliness.

"You seem to be an islander like Ron and me," Tam said. "You are our blood brother."

Ken had been thinking the same thing about Tam, for he seemed to know her as well as he knew the Mexican girl Rita, whose family lived on the Bar-H Ranch*, or Pago, the Navajo Indian who had helped him catch the black mustang. Ken liked Tamara as much as any girl he had even known, for he thought her able to do her part in any undertaking.

"Tam, can we make it to the island without the boat? You know the way?"

"Yes, you couldn't lose me in these waters, Ken, for I have swum in them all my life. Ron and I have the run of these islands and the water all the time, and we fish and play here many, many times together."

"O.K., let's get going then, or we might show up too late for breakfast. Here goes."

---

*This story is told in *KEN RIDES THE RANGE*.

Just as the Arizona lad prepared to dive overboard, Tam reminded him of the radio, adding, "What do you call it, the talkie-talk?"

"Walkie-talkie, you mean. That's right. Wonder if we could salvage anything of it?" he asked, slowly climbing over the litter from the machine gun bullets to the spot where he had first found the radio.

"Wow! They missed it clean as a whistle."

"You mean, Ken, it is all right and we can walkie-talkie with it?"

"Seems so," said Ken fingering the instrument. "Well, no, here is where a slug tore into it. But it might be worth salvaging. Reckon we could swim with it between us?"

While they were arguing for and against the idea of carrying the radio, weighing about fifty pounds, on their backs during the two-hour swim, Ken found a piece of canvas. It was waterproof.

"I got it, Tam. Here's what we can do: just what the army does when it has to swim across a river and carry guns and other equipment."

"And what's that, Ken?" she asked, eager to continue their adventure.

"They wrap up the stuff in canvas that'll keep the water out, and two soldiers swim with the floating bundle between them."

"But maybe this won't stay up . . . too heavy, Ken."

"That's right. So we'll have to take off all our extra clothes." He threw back his head and laughed, for his shirt was sleeveless, and his trousers were ripped to the knees. Tam was dressed modestly, yet simply, in a native dress, which came barely to her knees and was without sleeves. So "extra" clothes were out of the question, and Ken said so.

"Then we can wrap up something light, like a . . ." Tam

looked for anything that might increase the floating power of the radio. "Here it is, Ken, a . . . a . . . what do you call it?" Feeling the package she handed him, Ken said, "A cushion. Just the thing."

Together they wrapped the walkie-talkie and the cushion in the canvas, careful to make it as waterproof as possible, so that it would float. When they had finished with this task, they lifted the bundle to the boat's edge and prepared to let it slip overboard.

"We forgot something, American boy, and that's to pray."

"Right you are, Tam. We must ask God's blessing on this trip, 'cause it's a long ways and there are many dangers."

"Man-eaters . . ." added Tam.

Ken prayed:

"This is the only way, Lord, we can seem to make it. And Thou knowest how much we need the radio on the island. Maybe we can signal a PT boat or a submarine and they can come and rescue us from the island and get the penicillin to Australia where the boys need it so much. We ask Thee to keep the sharks out of our way and help us to get this bundle to the island. For Jesus' sake. Amen."

Ken heard Tam talking in her native tongue to the Master, and when she was finished, he said, "Tam, I can hear the words of Jesus when He said, *I am with you alway.*"

Dropping the bundle overboard, the two young people followed it into the water and began a long, tedious swim to the small island where they knew not what would await them.

"Swim one-handed, Ken, and we'll soon get it going."

Into the fog-dimmed night Ken and Tam, with a well packed walkie-talkie floating between them, set out to a distant island, which to each was the next step in fulfilling the American boy's service to God and country.

CHAPTER 6

RESCUED BY A PT BOAT

"I believe I got 'er this time, kids," Ken said.

The midafternoon sun was high, but Ken and the island boy and girl were covered by a thick canopy of palm fronds, which had hidden them from the relentless flying enemy patrol. How Ken and Tam were able to swim to the island, carrying between them the heavy walkie-talkie, they would never know. It had taken them more than twice as long to make the journey as Tamara had estimated, and several times only a towering wave and their ability to dive deep and swim under water for long periods of time had saved them from being sighted by the Japanese fighter planes which searched the ocean.

But they had made it by midmorning, and as Ken climbed out of the water, he believed himself to be more water-soaked than the canvas-wrapped radio. They had dragged themselves and the radio deep into the jungles where for hours they lay exhausted, too weary even to think of Ron's condition. Ken dropped into a deep sleep. The swim, coming so shortly after his rubber boat experience, had used all his strength. He felt himself being shaken, and looking up, he saw Tam's smiling face. She spoke:

"Ken, it's time to work on the talk-walk machine. Wake up."

The Arizona lad shook himself and leaped to his feet, saying, "I forgot all about Ron!"

At that instant Ken saw the native boy. He said, "How . . . I'm feelin' as you say it, no, K. O."

"You must mean 'O. K.', don't you?" Ken asked. The islander smiled and said, "Your medicine did it, no?"

"That's the finest medicine on earth to kill certain infections and germs," Ken said, referring to the penicillin. "And here's a living witness to it. Why, Dr. Jim said it simply stopped the germs from multiplying and a feller's red blood jumped into the fight and knocked out the rest uv the germs. Not very scientific, but that's what he said."

Ken continued to praise the healing power of the penicillin. "Over in America there was a little child that had one of them awful-soundin' diseases, scarcer than hens' teeth, and nothin' would help her, not even all those high-powered sulpha drugs, and they give her a couple shots of penicillin and she begun to mend right off.

"And another gal, 'bout your size and age, Tam, had a sure-killin' disease, and the army even furnished a plane and flew her to the Mayo Brothers Clinic, where they healed her by giving her penicillin."

Tam listened wide-eyed to Ken's talk, even though she did not understand all he said. The boy continued, speaking in Western style.

"The reason the army furnished the plane for the gal was because shortly before that she had cut off her long golden hair and given it to the army to make bomb sights to knock out the Japs and the Germans."

Much to the islanders' amazement, Tam touched the walkie-talkie. Ken patted his stomach, saying:

"I'm hollow as a well in here and just shore gotta have my backbone stretched away from my stomach before I go to work on 'er."

Tam realized that he meant he was hungry, and she stepped back among the palms and brought out a cracked-open coconut filled with nut milk.

"Drink," she said. When he had finished she went back to the kitchen hidden in the palms, and returned with a hollowed-out foot-long piece of bamboo, about four inches thick. Pulling out of one end several green banana leaves, which she had used as a stopper, the girl spread a large leaf on the ground and then shook out of the bamboo shoot something which Ken thought was a cooked banana, and another cooked substance that he was unable to identify.

"Breadfruit . . ." said Tam. "Good to eat, and you'd better fill up on it."

"What about you and Ron?"

"We ate long ago, while you slept."

Ken turned his attention to the radio. On the Bar-H, Les Lee, his uncle with whom he had lived, had given him a short-wave radio set and a shop in which to work. Night after night he had experimented with his radio.

Tam watched Ken's experienced fingers as they traced wires, tested tubes, looked for breaks in circuits.

"Yep, I've talked to people in almost every country with my short-wave set," Ken told the island youth as he tinkered with the radio. "And there is a girl about my age over in Australia that lives on a hundred-thousand-acre ranch that I shore did love to talk to. I promised to visit her sometime, when I got around to it, and I would like to go there on this trip."

"What's her name?" Tam asked.

"Karry Dare. How's that for a name, Tam?" Exploding like a firecracker with a short fuse, Ken exclaimed, "I got her. Right here's the trouble: this wire. It's the only break the bullet made. In a jiffy we'll be sending out a message."

True to his promise, Ken, after he had repaired the broken wire, turned a switch, and the power burst into the sending tubes. "We're on the air!" he said, turning off the current, for he did not want a listening Jap radioman to hear his words.

He decided to use only the word "penicillin" over and over again, hoping that some Australian station, or a bomber returning from a fighting mission over Jap-held territory or an American submarine would catch the words and contact him.

Ken snapped on the sending switch, but Ron stepped over and turned it off swiftly, saying, as he smiled at the American boy, "Talk to Jesus first."

"Righto you are, Ron. I was so much in a rush that I almost forgot about praying. Tam, you lead us in prayer." The girl prayed sincerely, in faultless English, a prayer which stirred Ken's heart. After asking that the radio might be heard and that deliverance might come, she concluded her prayer with the words ". . . that this wonderful medicine which saved Ron's life might be taken on to Australia where the boys are dying without it. Remember those soldiers, Jesus, and save them by Thy blood as our missionary told us. Amen."

Turning on the switch, Ken spoke distinctly into the microphone the word "penicillin," which sounded like "pennycillin," as it is pronounced. Meanwhile he turned on the receiving set and listened. He was able to contact various stations, some broadcasting in languages he could not understand, but Tam nodded her head as if to say, "I understand it."

"That's the Japanese telling about a battle they have lost to the Americans."

Ken turned the knob slightly to the right and heard a singer. Slowly trying various wave lengths, he listened as he spoke into the sender. Hour after hour he continued to send and listen, in what he thought was a vain effort to catch the attention of some American operator.

It was midnight, but Ken said the same word over and over. Suddenly he heard the word repeated. Just once. Then he spoke the word again and heard the same word in response.

"Ken Murray, Bar-H, penicillin," he said this time. "Come in, penicillin."

"What's Sandra's birthday?"

"We got 'em!" Ken shouted. "That's them. Sandra is my sister and they want to be sure I'm Ken Murray and not a Jap trying to lure a sub or PT or bomber over here to be blasted to pieces." He turned off the sending apparatus lest the enemy hear his conversation.

"October 14," Ken replied over the sending set.

"O. K., penicillin. Repeat word until further directions."

Ken repeated his code word over and over as the hours wore on, but he was unable to contact the other station again. He wondered if it could be a trap set by the Japs on the neighboring island, but he finally decided that they did not have a radio locating device or they would long ago have blasted the sending set.

Dawn came and still he said softly, "Penicillin, penicillin." Tamara and Ron doubled for him throughout the day, and when night came, Ken caught the words, "Penicillin. October 14, Sandra. What's Les Lee's phone number?"

"Desert View 45, ring two," Ken answered, giving the Bar-H local telephone number in Arizona.

"Give the Phoenix number," came in clearly over the receiving set.

"The Bar-H gotta direct line from Phoenix," he whispered to his island friends, and aloud he said into the sending microphone, "Phoenix Extension 2890."

"Righto!" burst from the receiving set. "In a half-hour be on the south end of the island."

"South end of the island?" Ken asked. "Where is that?" Ron answered by pointing toward where Ken thought Australia must be. "We've got 'er. They're comin' in after us. Reckon it's a sub or what?"

Meanwhile Tam handed the package of penicillin to Ken, saying, "Here, don't forget this. Ron, let's go and see what takes him to Australia."

"Takes me?" asked Ken. "How do you get that way? You're goin' along. I wouldn't have made it if it hadn't been for both of you, and they'll be wantin' to see you kids over in Australia. You just wait until those soldiers get this penicillin. You'll be the most loved and popular set of South Sea Island kids that ever lived! And besides, why can't you come to America? There's schools over there, and . . ."

"Do you suppose, Ken," Tamara began, "that I might go to one of those Christian training schools our missionary told us about, where I could be trained to be a nurse and Ron a doctor, so that we could come back to our own people as missionaries?"

"Shore, Uncle Les'll do hit. He's richer than gravy, and since he got saved, he just loves doin' things for Jesus that cost money."

Slowly they made their way through the tangle of palms and jungle vines. Tam carried the package of penicillin, and Ken, the walkie-talkie. Ron, his good arm around his sister's neck, walked beside her. When they came to the edge of the jungle, they walked out on the island's southernmost tip, where they stood on the beach, waiting for their rescuer.

The sound of motors near by caused Ken, as he later said, "to almost jump out of my skin." Looking toward a small cove which was completely overhung by jungle vines, he saw a long, low, powerfully built PT boat.

Three sailors jumped into the waters and swam ashore. The captain standing on deck shouted, "O. K., kids, let's get going."

Two sailors relieved Tam and Ken of their burdens, while the third, seeing that Ron was injured, swam with the lad to the boat, Tam and Ken cutting their way through the waters toward the answer to their prayers.

CHAPTER 7

AUSTRALIA AT LAST

"Boy, did you have us worried all night," said the captain as Ken and the islanders came aboard. "We caught your message early yesterday afternoon just as you came on the air, but were afraid that it was a Jap trap."

"How did you happen to be on the wave length of this walkie-talkie we captured from the enemy patrol?" asked Ken.

"When the B-17 didn't show up at Island X as it was supposed to, the army and navy organized the greatest manhunt ever conducted anywhere in the world—even greater than the one that looked all over the South Pacific for Rickenbacker and his companions. We covered every possible sector where you might have gone down. Then the FBI caught a sabotage ring in Washington, D. C., that had learned of the purpose and route of your flight to Australia with the penicillin."

"Captain, that explains why the bomber's navigator did not hit the mystery island, doesn't it?"

"Sure does, Ken. Navy Intelligence in Honolulu picked up the little sister who queered his instruments, and she has gone in for a lifetime spy sentence. All this gave us our clue, for she confessed she altered the instruments so they would land your bomber far north of Island X, and Japanese navy fliers were tailing your position all the time. When we contacted your radio, the FBI furnished us with the catch questions about Sandra's birthday and the ranch phone numbers. This was information they said nobody but you could possibly have."

At length the captain explained to Ken the mystery of the wrecked Flying Fortress, telling Ken that a searching plane had located the three life rafts in which the fliers had been strafed and killed by a Japanese plane.

"We haven't located Major Kenedy as yet," said the captain. Ken explained, "He went down with the plane, for I saw him lying on the bomber's floor just before it sank. His skull was crushed."

Meanwhile the PT boat sped through the waters at better than sixty knots an hour, heading directly toward Australia. Ken thought he had never been on a beast, plane, train or boat that cut so many capers in leaping waves and crashing through mountains of water as the PT did. It was thrilling to him and the island young people to stand with the captain and crewmen on the deck and watch the breakers go by.

"Some speed," remarked Ken to Tamara. A sailor standing near by heard him and answered, "I should say, for we are being tailed by half the Japanese navy unless the skipper misses his guess. The reason we didn't reveal our identity any sooner than we did was the fact that two Jap subs were after us all the time, knowing that we had located something connected with the precious drug."

"How long were you hidden in the cove?" asked the island girl, who on the boat had said little.

"All night. We got in early after dark, and tried to ferret out the identity of the sending set that was cracking back and forth with that drug's name."

"Stand by for action!" called a crewman. "Periscope on the starboard!"

Looking toward the spot located by a pointing sailor, Ken and his friends saw the ugly wet snout of a Jap submarine, and suddenly Ken saw a streak of something cut through the waters from the sub's belly and drive at an amazing speed directly toward the PT boat's path.

"Torpedo!"

"Fire tube I!" commanded an officer. Then came an explosion which almost lifted the boat out of the water. Toward the submarine sped the PT's torpedo just as that fired by the submarine struck a few yards behind the PT.

"A near miss," said the captain, as he watched the submarine's snout drop below the water's edge. In a second or two there was a loud report in the distance and a shower of water arose where the sub had gone down.

"Looks like a hit," remarked someone, but the captain added, "We're in too big a hurry getting out of here to go back and see." Speaking into the tube, he ordered, "Full speed ahead."

"The Japs have done everything to try to keep this penicillin from reaching the base hospital, but thanks to you, lad, it looks like the boys over there will soon be out of their misery."

"How far is it, Captain, to Australia?"

"About two hundred miles, Ken, to the nearest tip of land, but several hundred more to the hospital. We have just broken radio silence and sent a message of your discovery to the outside world, also a request that a bomber and fighter escort meet us as soon as possible and fly you to the hospital."

That was the best news Ken had received. He could almost see the end of his mission, and when he returned to America he could look the general in the face and say, "Mission completed."

"But don't think this race is over yet, Ken. If I don't miss my guess you are liable to see some fireworks from Japanese planes. But we've got as good a crew of antiaircraft gunners as ride the ocean, and they will do their best to see us through."

Going below, Ken saw the radio operator record a message, and a crewman said, "Message coming through." Ken waited tensely, wondering what it could be, and hoping it was good news.

The captain came into the room, and the operator handed him a report. "Message, sir, from General MacArthur."

The captain read the message silently and then said, "Ken, this is for you and your island friends. Shall I read it to you?"

Ken nodded and the captain read:

"Congratulations to Ken Murray on the successful near-completion of your mission. We are sending a bomber escort to pick you up. Regards to your fine helpers from the island. Signed, General Douglas MacArthur."

Ken was thrilled. He felt something fill his eyes, and the room grew hazy.

"Any message you want to send the general, or anywhere?" asked the captain.

"Tell him thanks, and to ask the boys to hold on a little longer, for the penicillin is on its way. And . . . and is more than a match for any Japanese poisoned bullets, for it cured my island friend of the same kind of wound."

"By this time, young fellow, you are the most popular boy in the world. You have done what few if any men have accomplished in their lives. You have proved yourself worthy . . ."

The captain's words were cut short by the message coming over the loud speaker: "Enemy aircraft overhead!"

"Man the guns!"

Soon Ken felt the boat shake under the constant fire of the PT's antiaircraft guns. The captain had gone on deck, but commanded Ken and the other young people to stay below. Looking through the open hatchway, Ken saw a dive bomber race through the skies at the speed of four hundred miles an hour. The plane was headed straight for the boat. It looked as if the end had come.

Just before the bomber pulled out of its dive and dropped its bombs, Ken saw it explode in midair, a long shroud of black smoke enveloping it as it crashed into the sea.

Ken prayed earnestly. Then there came to him the assurance which God had given long before, the promise that He would see him safely through to Australia and give him the privilege of bringing the Gospel's message of cheer and salvation to the wounded men. The penicillin would heal their bodies, and Christ would heal their souls.

Tamara, stepping to the deck, heard the roar of planes flying at a low altitude from the south, and soon Ken could see what looked like a skyful of planes, fighters and bombers, which were coming, he hoped, to help him fulfill his mission safely.

Sighting the PT boat, the bombers circled overhead. The fighter escorts swarmed around them, and Ken saw one ship, larger than the others, cut into the waters to land.

"General MacArthur's private plane, Ken, if I'm not mistaken," said the pilot.

Taxiing closer to the boat, the plane drew as near as possible.

The PT boat dropped overboard a large rubber craft, into which sailors helped Ken and his companions. Soon they were rowed to the bomber, and lifted carefully into the plane. The engines roared, and the ship pushed through the waves until it was able to break water and rise into the sky. Circling for altitude, the bomber set a direct course for Australia. In less than an hour Ken saw a long reef which seemed to stretch for miles, and beyond it was land.

Australia, he thought, *here I come!* There it was below him—the land which was the most welcome sight on earth at that moment.

He and Tamara, seated side by side, were an odd-looking pair. Their clothes had been torn to tatters by the long swim, and Ken's arm had been cut from shoulder to wrist. The cut had been made by a shark's fin when he and Tam had delivered the walkie-talkie to the island.

Following the line of Australia's shore, Ken saw the outlines of a frontier town and the co-pilot said, "Cooktown." The tropical beauty thrilled Ken. Soon the plane turned landward from Cooktown and edged toward a mountain which seemed to rise before them and block their passage.

Ken knew that somewhere in that beautiful North Queensland, Australia—in the land of kangaroos, gold mining, cattle raising and sheep herding—was the hospital, carefully protected from the enemy by camouflage.

Into Ken's mind came the words: *I will bless the Lord at all times: his praise shall continually be in my mouth.* He was happy, for he had done what God wanted him to do. Looking at the altimeter, he saw it reach 10,000, then jump by degrees to 9,000 and suddenly point to 4,000. Ken knew the plane was beginning to level off for a landing. The ground seemed to leap at him, and before he knew it he felt the giant bomber speed along the runway and come to a stop.

When the door was opened, the pilot sent Ken out first, and he was greeted by a great crowd of soldiers who cried:

"Welcome to Australia!"

The first hand that touched his was General MacArthur's. He had flown to the hospital so that he could more effectively direct the search.

"There they are, Ken," said the general. "They want *you*. You are their hero today. You have finished a mission, one of the most difficult any man ever undertook. You have not made it possible to conquer a continent like North Africa or Italy. But you have done far more. You have brought life and hope to the wounded boys who are bringing freedom's hope to all the world enslaved by the Japanese. The blessings of God be upon you."

Before Ken could answer the general, Tamara, clutching the precious penicillin, stepped to his side, and said, "Ken, remember, this is what you came to bring to these wounded soldiers."

Ken took the package, and with Tamara on one side and Ron on the other, the three marched through a suddenly opened lane between the soldiers. With their heads held high but their hearts humble before the Lord, they walked eagerly to the entrance of the hospital, where many thousands awaited the life-giving medicine Ken had risked his life to bring them, and for which ten brave men had given their lives.

"Reporting, sir, for Major James Kenedy, who died in line of duty," said Ken, handing the penicillin to the commanding officer who had met them at the hospital's entrance.

"You have done well, young man, and I shall immediately order the medicine administered to the wounded men, who are clamoring to see the boy who has brought them the hope of life. They all want you to visit them, and I am sure your presence and that of your companions will be a great blessing to them." The officer introduced the trio to an attendant, who was to show them to their quarters. But as they started for the suite of rooms which the hospital staff had set aside for them, another officer said, "If you feel like it, the men are calling for you right now as you are. Will you follow me?"

Nothing could have delighted Ken more than this, and in spite of his torn clothes, he went from bedside to bedside, and spoke words of Christian comfort to each of the suffering men. Though he did not have time to linger beside each bed as he desired, he knew that in the days to come he would be able to come back and bring the Christian message of salvation to them.

There were hundreds of wounded soldiers, whom Ken loved as he loved his own life, who had read their Testaments in the foxholes, prayed prayers of confession, and had accepted Christ by faith and been saved. Ken wanted to pray with them that their faith in Christ might be strengthened, and in his heart was a prayer that Christ might save the others also.

Having made their visits, Ken and his island companions went to the suite, which consisted of two rooms, one for Tamara and one for the boys, opening off a large sitting room. Coming out of Tamara's room was a beautiful girl, about Tamara's age, who offered her hand to Ken and said, "I'm Karry Dare, and I know you are Ken Murray. I am here to welcome you to my homeland and invite you out to our ranch when you care to come. And I want your friends to come with you."

Tamara stood back for a moment, and then Karry put her arm around the island girl. "You're lovely, and I am sure America and Australia are proud of the fine part you have played, both you and your brother, in helping Ken deliver the penicillin to these suffering soldiers."

Ken was too stunned to speak. He had finished his mission of love and mercy for his country and had been guided by his Heavenly Father, who supplied every need. As he sat down, with Ron at his side, he saw Karry lead Tam into her room, and while he sat, filled with gratitude, he rested, ready at a moment's notice to drop into a long sleep.

As he looked up, two lovely girls met his eyes. One was Karry, but he thought, *Who is the other?* The Australian girl answered the question by saying, "Meet my new sister, Tamara." A complete outfit of Karry's attractive clothes had transformed Tamara.

"Ken, I am awfully glad you came," began Karry, a worried look coming into her eyes. "I'm in dreadful trouble out at the ranch. Will you help me?"

There was only one answer for Ken. Having fulfilled one mission, he was certain there would be strength to undertake another, and he said, "Yep, let me get the sea water out of my legs and I'll be your Australian cowboy."

Printed in the United States of America